PHILLIP THE FLOWER-EATING PHOENIX

BY JOHN TODARO AND BARBARA ELLEN
PICTURES BY JOHN TODARO   ABELARD-SCHUMAN
LONDON NEW YORK TORONTO

THE STATE LIBRARY
65 S. FRONT ST.
COLUMBUS 15, OHIO

opyright 1961 by John Todaro and Barbara Ellen/Library of Congress Catalogue Card Number: 61:13320/Printed in the United States of America

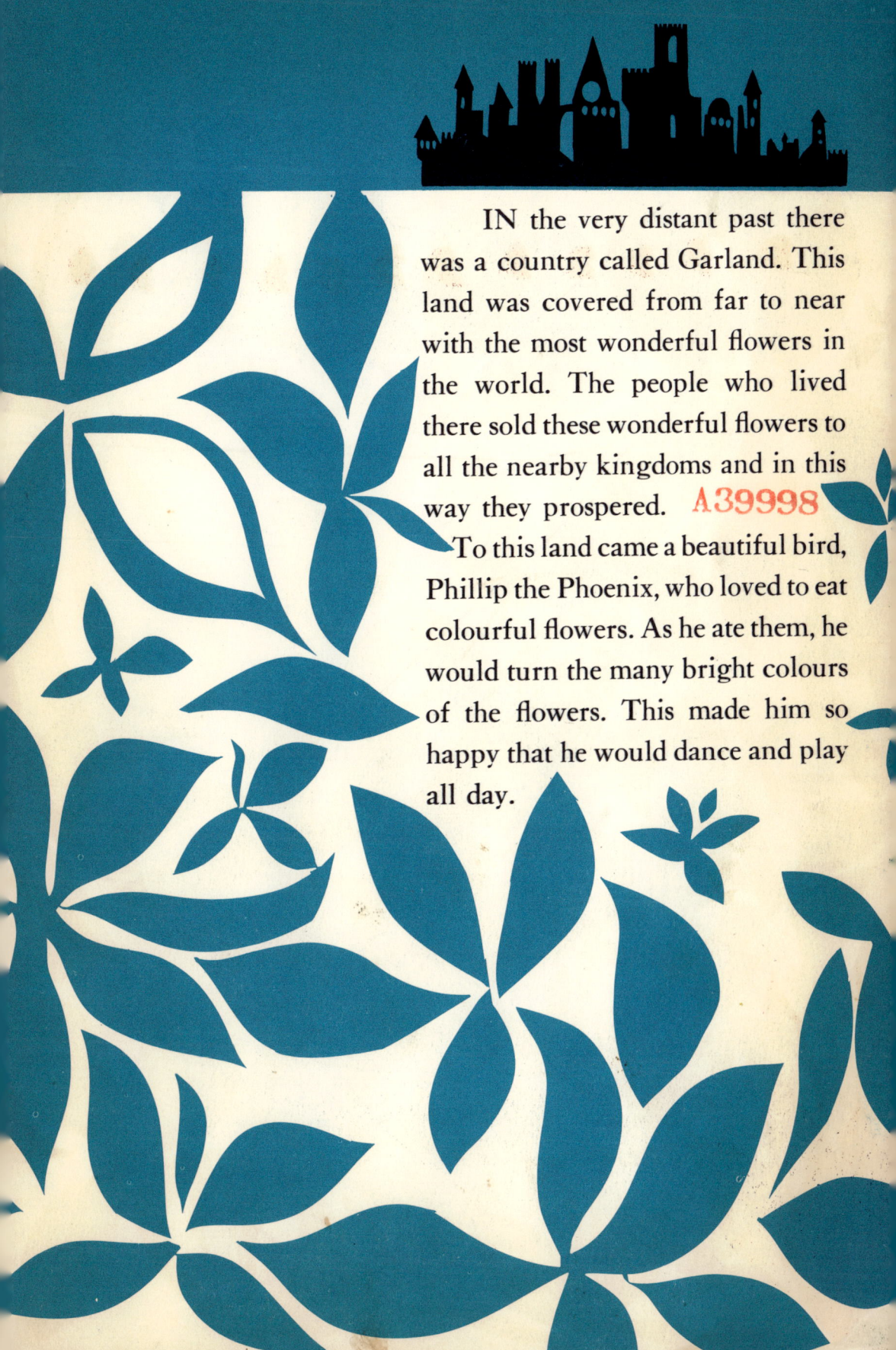

IN the very distant past there was a country called Garland. This land was covered from far to near with the most wonderful flowers in the world. The people who lived there sold these wonderful flowers to all the nearby kingdoms and in this way they prospered. A39998

To this land came a beautiful bird, Phillip the Phoenix, who loved to eat colourful flowers. As he ate them, he would turn the many bright colours of the flowers. This made him so happy that he would dance and play all day.

The people of Garland were not happy when they saw Phillip the Phoenix eating their flowers. They chased him and he ran and hid among the flower beds.

The people searched the flower beds and the forests — everywhere they thought a Phoenix might hide. But Phillip was too clever for them. Since the people could not find him, they went to the King.

"The Phoenix is eating all our flowers and we shall have none to sell. What shall we do?"

The King replied, "Do not worry. I shall send my soldiers to capture the Flower-Eating Phoenix."

Out of the castle marched the soldiers. They searched and searched. They climbed up the bell tower, looked under all the staircases and peered in every well, but they could not find Phillip the Flower-Eating Phoenix.

Phillip was much too clever for them, and the soldiers returned unsuccessfully to the King.

The King then proclaimed: "To the brave knight who captures Phillip the Phoenix I will give half my kingdom and the hand of my daughter, Princess Paulette, in marriage."

First came Sir Arnold, a brave knight who had fought many dragons. He found Phillip the Phoenix eating in a large field of daisies. He tried to tiptoe behind Phillip and grab him. SNAP! Sir Arnold stepped on a twig, and Phillip ran as fast as he could into a thicket of thistles. The foolish knight followed but he did not get very far before he began to itch and itch and itch all over. Phillip left the thicket, while Sir Arnold remained scratching away.

Then Sir Hugo, an old knight with a long, flowing beard, came to try his luck, but Phillip was much too fast for him. He chased Phillip through the tulip beds, the poppy fields, in and out of the lilac bushes, and finally into a patch of morning-glories, where his beard became entangled in the clinging vines. He tugged and pulled but he only became more and more entangled, while Phillip ran happily away.

Sir Duncan, a young knight seeking fame and fortune, came next to Garland to capture Phillip the Phoenix. He chased poor Phillip in and out of every flower bed in Garland. Phillip was nearly exhausted, but then it began to rain. Sir Duncan was still chasing Phillip when suddenly the knight froze. His armour had rusted solid. Phillip was able to get away.

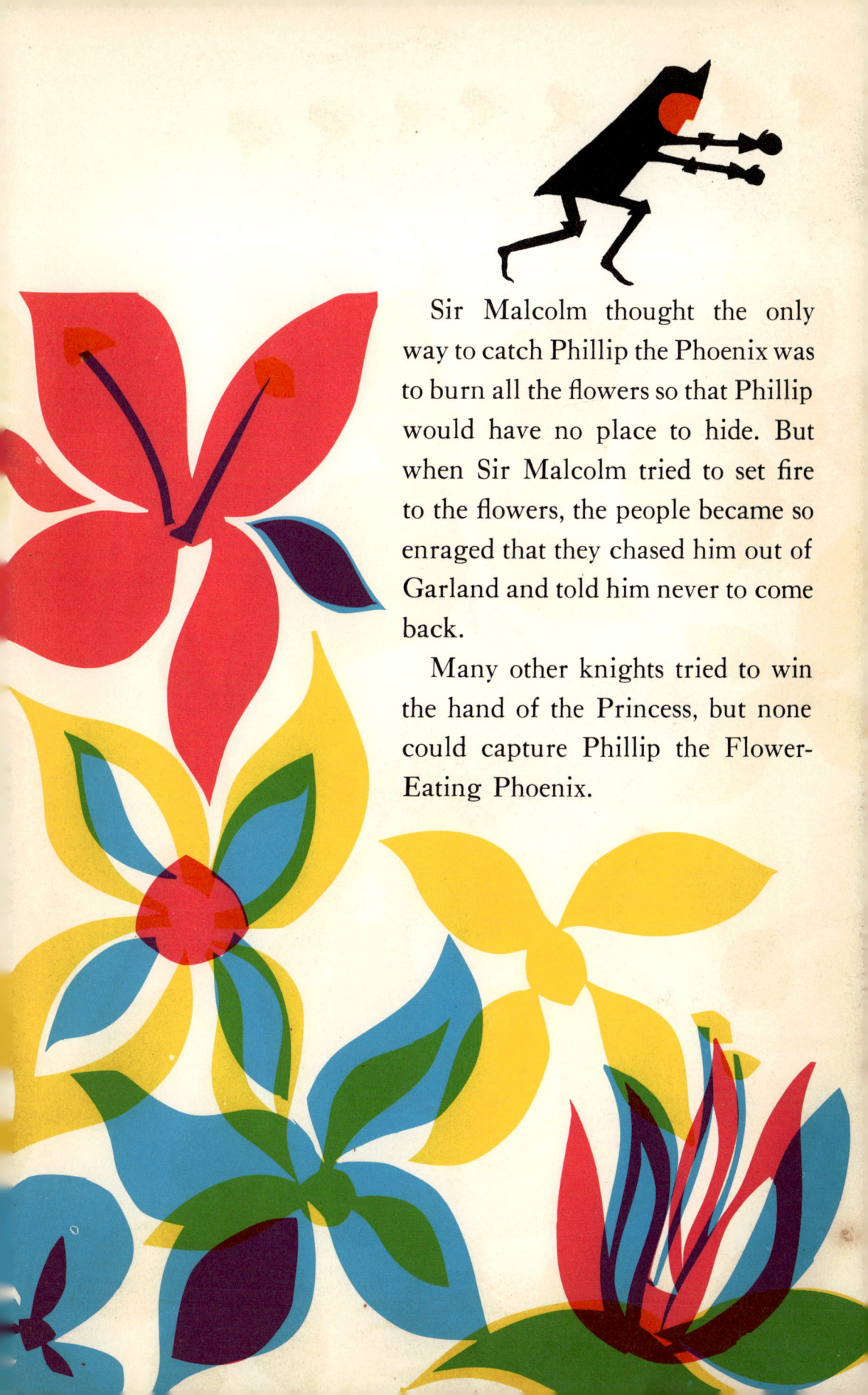

Sir Malcolm thought the only way to catch Phillip the Phoenix was to burn all the flowers so that Phillip would have no place to hide. But when Sir Malcolm tried to set fire to the flowers, the people became so enraged that they chased him out of Garland and told him never to come back.

Many other knights tried to win the hand of the Princess, but none could capture Phillip the Flower-Eating Phoenix.

The King realized Phillip the Phoenix was much too clever for the knights so he sent for the Court Magician, Marmaduke.

Now Marmaduke was evil and had learned when he was apprentice to The Great Wizard that a Phoenix has the secret of eternal life. He wanted this secret so that he too could live forever and become the evil ruler of Garland.

The King looked at Marmaduke the Magician and said, "None of the knights have been able to capture Phillip the Phoenix. I don't know what to do."

"Do not worry," said the Magician. "I know of one knight who can save Garland from this Phoenix. He is my nephew, Sir Nicholas Henry William de Vere."

"I only hope he can," said the King. "Send for him right away."

"Yes," thought the crafty Magician, "he will capture Phillip, but for *me*," and he crept up the tower stairs to his room.

Now Sir Nicholas was a goodly knight. He was so gentle that he would not even fight fiery dragons, because he did not want to hurt them. Marmaduke chose him because he was his nephew. He knew Sir Nicholas would obey him if he thought no one would be harmed.

So Marmaduke persuaded Sir Nicholas to come to Garland and help capture Phillip the Flower-Eating Phoenix.

Marmaduke the Magician brought his nephew before the King.

"This is Sir Nicholas Henry William de Vere, who will rid the kingdom of that flower-eating fiend," said the Magician.

"Good, good, good!" said the King, clapping his hands and dancing up and down on his throne. "Go now and bring the Phoenix to me as soon as you capture him."

"I," said Marmaduke the Magician, "will tell you how to capture Phillip the Phoenix."

"I don't want to hurt him, Uncle," wept Sir Nicholas.

"You won't have to hurt him. Now dry your eyes," said Marmaduke. "That's no way for a brave knight to act. Don't you want to win the hand of the Princess Paulette and live happily ever after, as the noble knights do in all the fairy tales?"

"Yes!" cried Sir Nicholas. "But how can I capture the Phoenix, when so many other knights have tried and failed?"

"Listen to my plan," said the Magician. "Every afternoon the Princess Paulette goes to the royal garden to pick flowers. She puts the flowers into a basket. Then she goes for a walk in the woods. I've cut a little hole in the bottom of the basket. One by one the flowers will fall out as she walks and will leave a trail." Marmaduke handed Sir Nicholas a large brown sack.

"Phillip will see the flowers," he continued, "and when he starts to eat them, throw this over him and bring him to me. Hurry now! But be sure to bring him to me first!"

Sir Nicholas went off to the woods and hid behind some bushes.

Soon he saw the Princess walking through the woods leaving a trail of beautiful flowers. There, following a short distance behind her, was Phillip, the dreaded Flower-Eating Phoenix of Garland. As Sir Nicholas peeped through the bushes he thought, "I hope he doesn't eat knights too! Yet, he doesn't look frightening. In fact, he looks rather funny. I'm sure I can capture him."

Sir Nicholas now disguised himself as a tree. The Princess passed by him. Following very closely came Phillip the Flower-Eating Phoenix. He was eating the flowers as they fell from the basket and as he ate them, he changed into their colours.

Then, as Phillip passed by, out jumped Sir Nicholas. Before Phillip knew what was happening Sir Nicholas threw the sack over him and tied the top tight.

The Princess saw what had happened and cried out, "Do not harm him. He is my friend! I come here to the woods every day to give him the most colourful flowers I can find in the royal garden."

"I shall not hurt the Phoenix. I'm just going to take him to my Uncle Marmaduke," replied Sir Nicholas.

"Please," wept the Princess, "you must take Phillip to my father the King. I do not trust Marmaduke the Magician."

Sir Nicholas could not bear to see Princess Paulette cry.

"Please stop crying," he pleaded as he handed her his handkerchief. "I'll take him to the King if you want me to."

"Yes," she said as she dried her tears with Sir Nicholas' handkerchief.

Sir Nicholas tried to lift the sack but found that it was much too heavy to carry. Then he cut two holes in the bottom of the sack so that Phillip could walk, using his own legs.

Off they went to the castle, with Sir Nicholas holding one end of a long rope. On the other end was a large brown sack with legs.

The King and all the Court were waiting for Sir Nicholas to return. At last he did come, but he was not alone. Proudly he marched up to the King. He was accompanied by Princess Paulette and a big brown bag with legs. Triumphantly he stated:

"Sire, I have captured the Flower-Eating Phoenix of Garland." Then he handed the rope to the King.

"That doesn't look much like the Flower-Eating Phoenix to me," said the King. "It looks like a big brown sack."

"It is a big brown sack. The Phoenix is inside," said Sir Nicholas.

He opened the top of the bag and tied the rope around Phillip's neck.

"Yes, yes, of course..." the King said, blushing.

"Why have you been eating the flowers in my kingdom?" demanded the King.

"Yes, why have you been eating the flowers in our kingdom?" echoed the people.

A large tear rolled down from Phillip's eye as he spoke:

"Everything in the world has a colour of its own: the animals, the trees, the sky and the flowers. But I have no colour of my own and this makes me very sad. But when I eat the beautifully coloured flowers, I become all their bright colours. It makes me so happy to have a colour that I dance and play among the flowers all day."

Then everyone began to notice that Phillip was not beautiful any more. His colours had been slowly fading away until he was now just a drab, colourless bird. Phillip started to cry harder, and the King had tears in his eyes. The soldiers and all the people began to weep. The fair Princess was sobbing, and the brave Sir Nicholas was crying hardest of all.

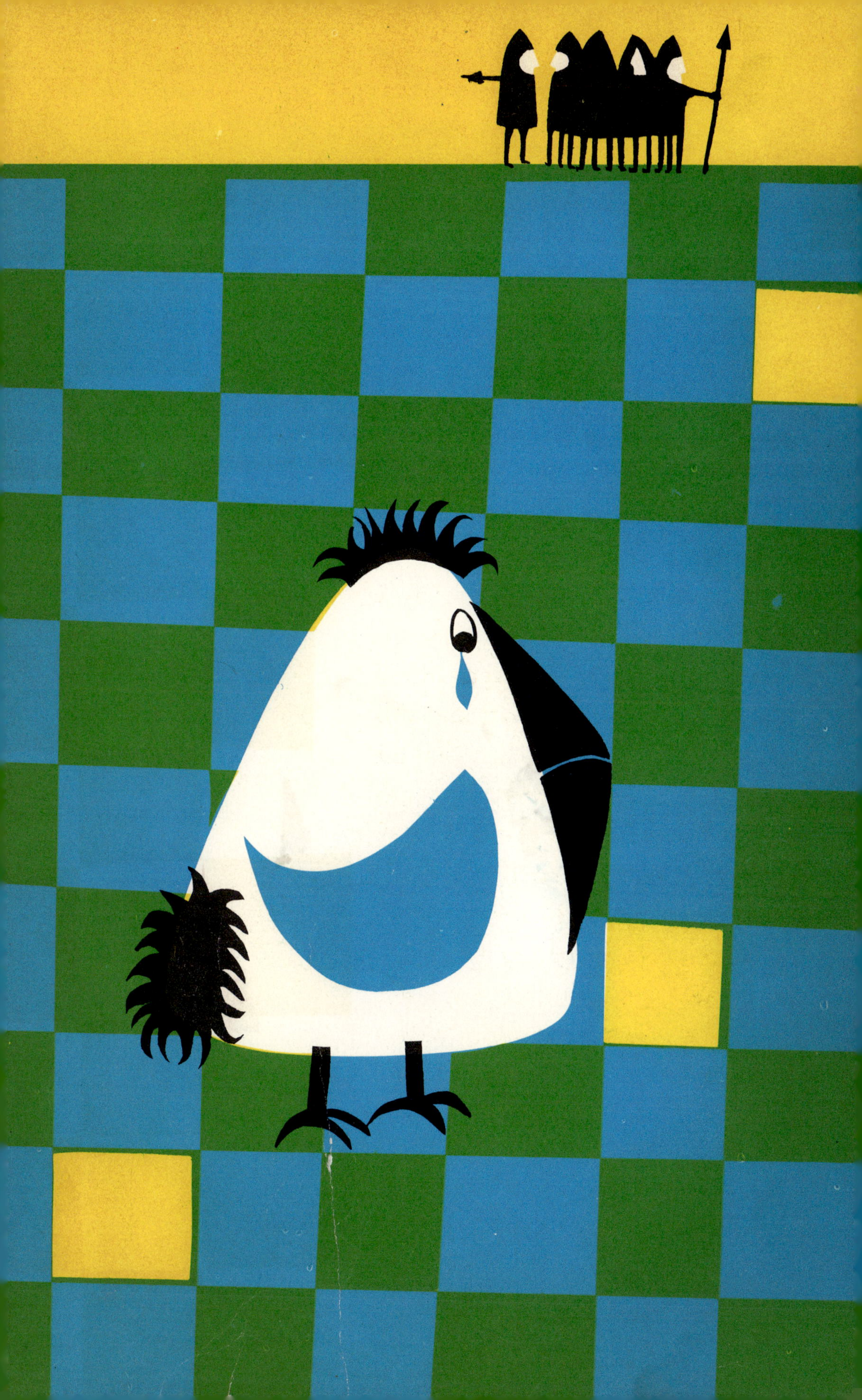

The only person who was not crying was Marmaduke the Magician. He exclaimed, "Why are you all so sad? You should be rejoicing now that the Phoenix has been captured! Give him to me and I shall rid the kingdom of this flower-eating fiend!"

He grabbed the rope from the King and started to drag poor Phillip toward the tower.

"Stop him!" cried the Princess. "He'll hurt Phillip! He knows a Phoenix can live forever and he wants this knowledge for himself so that he can live forever and rule over Garland."

"I'll stop him," shouted Sir Nicholas.

Crash! Thump! went the wicked Magician as Sir Nicholas threw the same brown sack over him that he had used to capture Phillip the Phoenix. Sir Nicholas was getting quite good at using it.

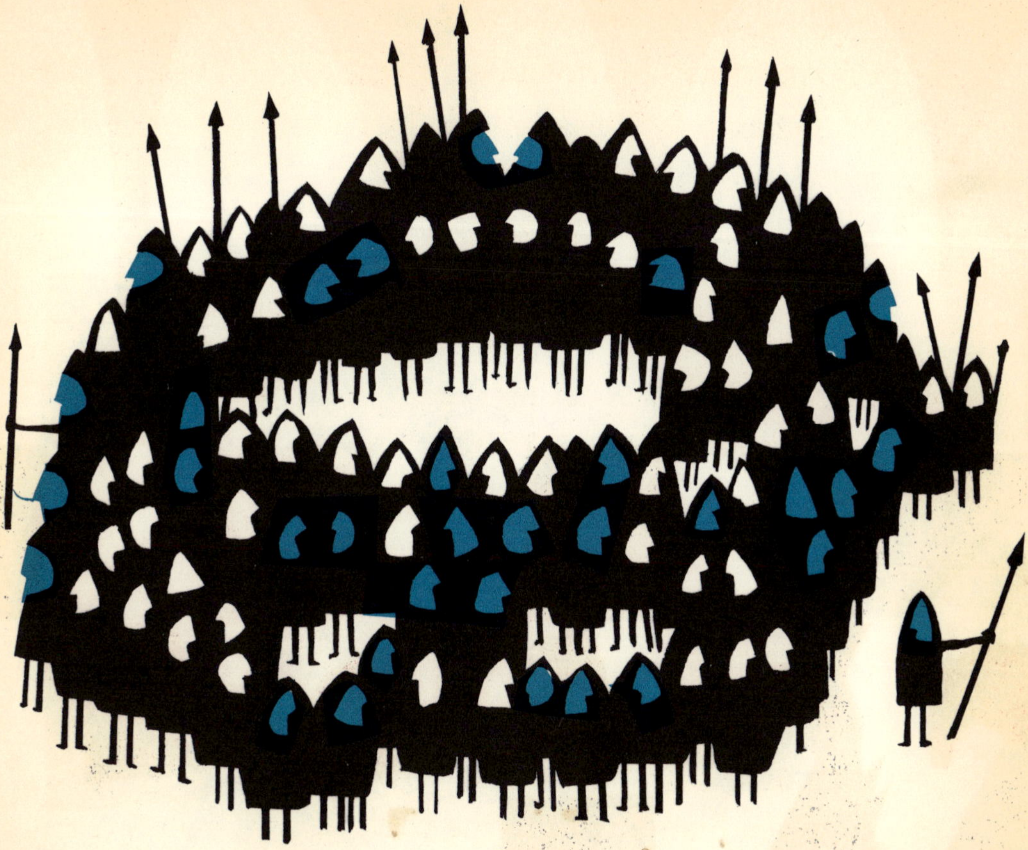

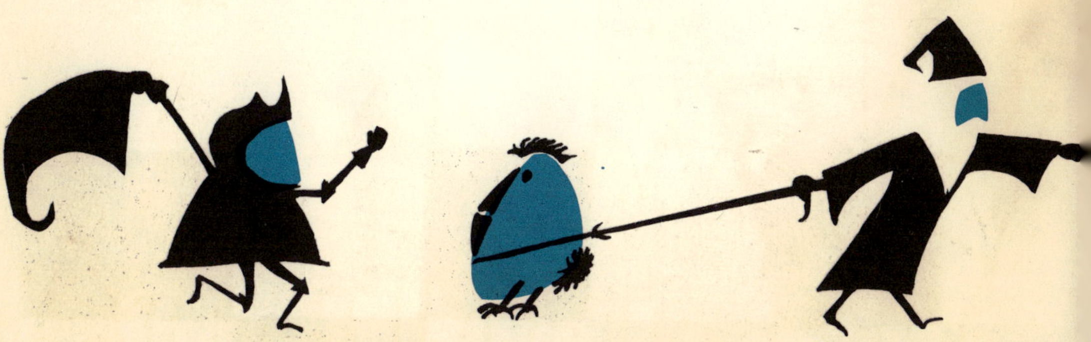

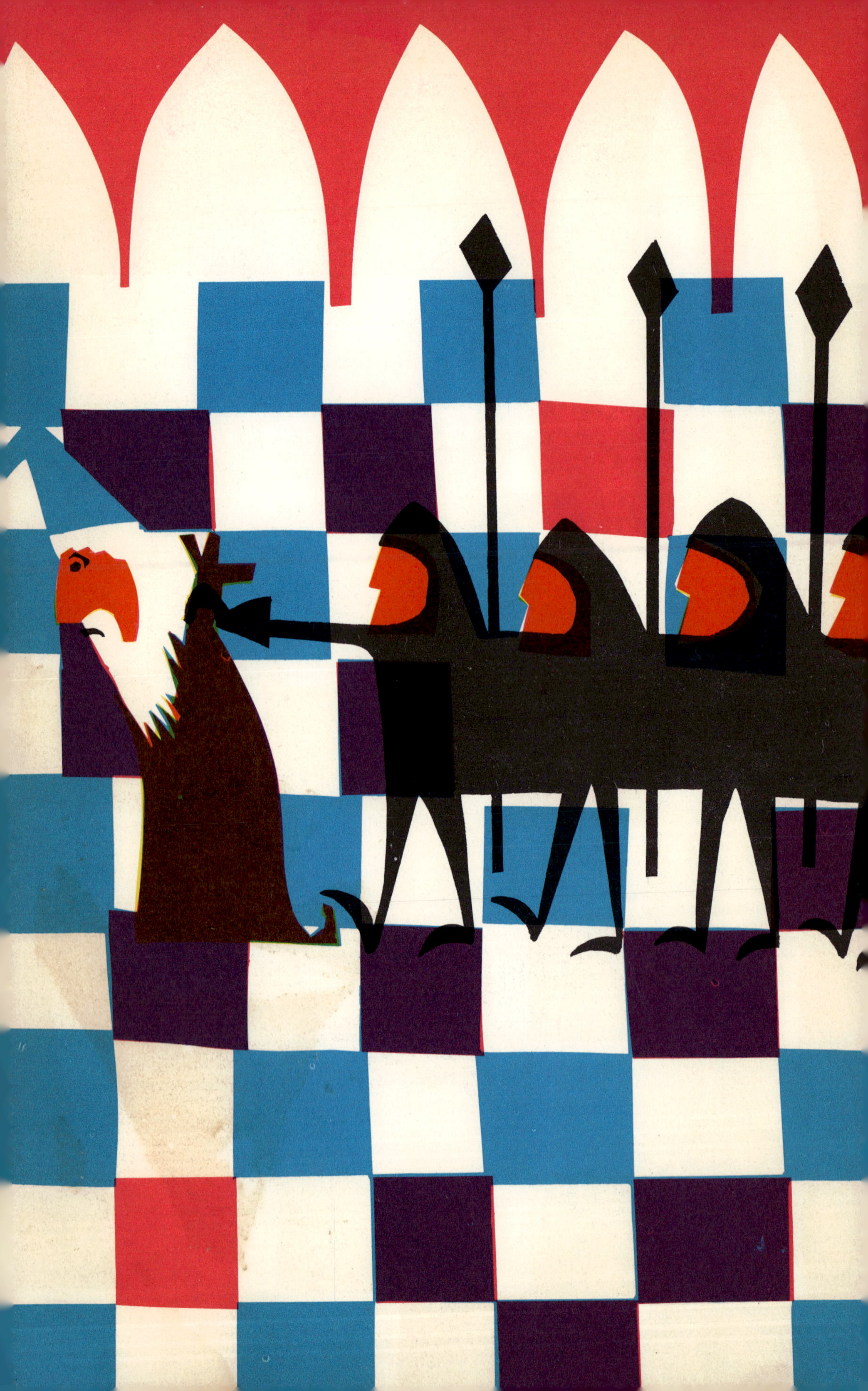

He brought Marmaduke before the King, and the King declared: "Marmaduke, you are an evil man and I must banish you from Garland forever." Quickly, the soldiers took him away.

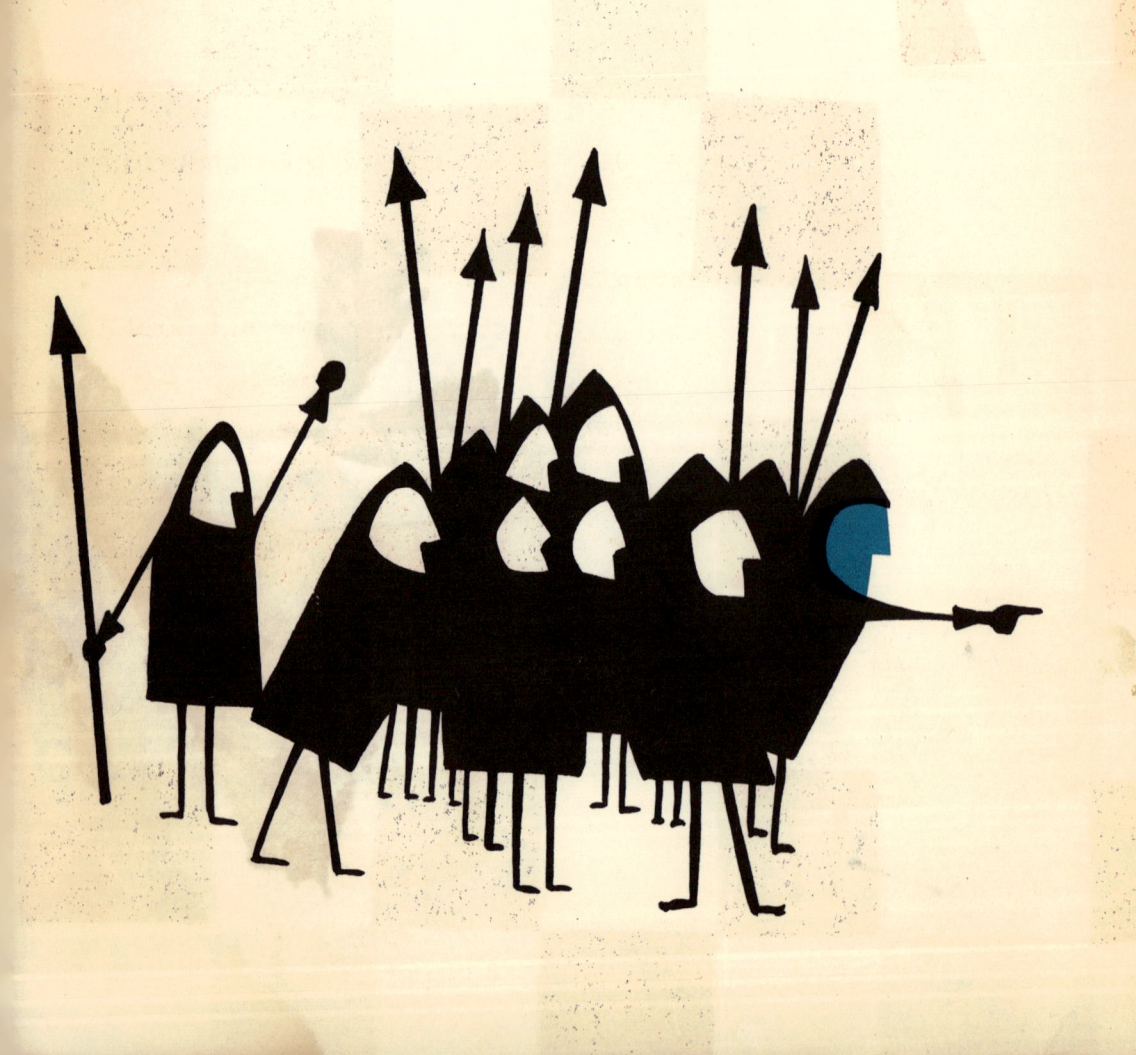

Then the King turned to Phillip and asked, "Is it true that you can live forever and give others this wonderful gift?"

Phillip answered solemnly, "It is true I have eternal life but I cannot give it to others. I do not know why I can live forever any more than a tree knows why it is tall, or the grass knows why it is green.

"I can't tell others how to live forever any more than they can tell me how *not* to live forever. This gift isn't as wonderful as you think, for I have lived so long that there is no freshness or colour in my own life. That is why I must eat flowers—to give my life colour."

Sir Nicholas and Princess Paulette approached the King.

"Sire, we have one wish—that Phillip may have a garden of his own to dance and play in and all the most beautiful flowers to eat."

The King answered, "Your wish is granted, for all things should have colour."

The King set Phillip free and asked him to stay for the wedding of his daughter to Sir Nicholas. All the people cheered.

And Phillip the Flower-Eating Phoenix was given a garden of his own to live in, with all the beautiful flowers he could eat.